W9-APS-655

Disney's Millennium Year Book 2000

GROLIER BOOKS

Published by Grolier Books
Grolier Books is a division of Grolier Enterprises, Inc.

Fern L. Mamberg   *Executive Editor*
Elizabeth A. DeBella   *Designer*
Barbara L. Persan   *Production Manager*

ISBN: 0-7172-8968-0
ISSN: 0273-1274

Stories on pages 16–27, 36–47, 48–53, 58–69, 78–89, and all Disney character illustrations copyright © 2000 by Disney Enterprises, Inc.

Pages 16–27 written by Victoria Saxon. © 2000 Burroughs and Disney. Tarzan® Owned by Edgar Rice Burroughs, Inc. and Used by Permission
Pages 36–47 written by Amy Bauman. Based on the Pooh stories by A. A. Milne, © The Pooh Properties Trust
Pages 58–69 written by Barbara Bazaldua
Pages 78–89 written by Liane Onish
Stories illustrated by Alvin S. White Studio

Illustration Credits and Acknowledgments

6–11: Artist, Vince Caputo. 12: © Richard Kolar/Animals Animals; © Antje Gunnar/ Bruce Coleman Inc. 13: © Phyllis Greenberg/Animals Animals. 14: © Tui DeRoy/ Bruce Coleman Inc. 15: © Frans Lanting/Photo Researchers, Inc. 28–29: From *Make Cards!* © 1991 by F&W Publications. Used by permission of North Light Books, a division of F&W Publications, Inc. 30–31: Fabrice Coffini/AP/Wide World Photos. 30: © Yvain Genevay/Sipa. 31: Artist, Gary Torrisi. 32: © 1999 Time Inc. Reprinted by permission. 33: © Brian Stablyk/Tony Stone Images. 34: © Zig Leszczynski/ Animals Animals; © Joseph Van Wormer/Bruce Coleman Inc. 35: © Patti Murray/ Animals Animals; © James H. Robinson/Animals Animals. 54: © Douglas Faulkner/ Photo Researchers, Inc. 55: © Theodore L. Manekin/TLM Productions. 56: Nina Fuller/The Liaison Agency; © Chris Luneski/Image Cascade. 56–57: © Theodore L. Manekin/TLM Productions. 57: © Theodore L.Manekin/TLM Productions. 70–71: Designed by Jenny Tesar; Artist, Natasha Lessnik Tibbott. 72: © Michael Dick/Animals Animals. 73: © Neal J. Menschel/*Christian Science Monitor.* 74: © Michael Dick/Animals Animals; © Renee Lynn/Photo Researchers, Inc. 75: © S. Michael Bisceglie/Animals Animals. 76: Zig Leszczynski/Animals Animals. 77: © Michael Habicht/Animals Animals. 90–95: NASA.

Contents

Into the Future!

What if you had lived 1,000 years ago. Can you imagine what life was like then? There were no telephones or computers. There were no cars, planes, trains, or bikes. There was no ice cream or popcorn. There were no radios to listen to. No televisions to watch. No movies to see. No air-conditioners to cool you off.

Lots of wonderful things were invented between the years 1000 and 1999. Now we are entering the year 2000. It's a very special time. The year 2000 marks the beginning of a **millennium**—a period of 1,000 years.

What will life be like in the next 1,000 years? Will our lives change a lot? Some experts think so. And they say that the biggest changes will come about because of computers. In fact, computers will be king!

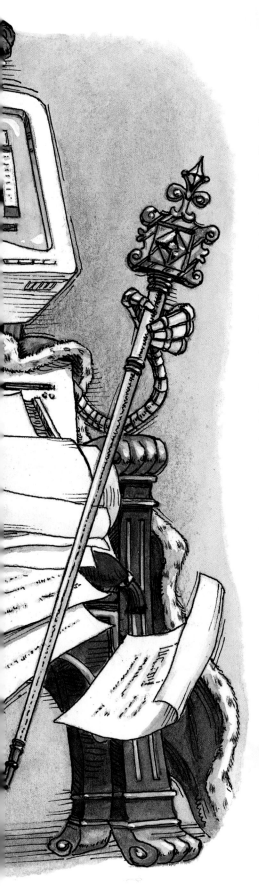

At Home. Millions of people have computers today. But in the future, everyone will *have* to have one. Computers will be part of just about everything we do. And they'll be smaller and much more powerful than the ones we have now.

You'll probably have a complex computer system in your home. It will keep the family records and link you to the Internet. It will turn out the lights and adjust the temperature. It will control your TV, VCR, and sound system. But what if you want to watch TV and your sister wants to link to her favorite Web site? No problem. Several display screens will be mounted on the walls in different parts of your house. So everyone in your family can watch different things at the same time.

Computers will still have keyboards, mice, and remote controls. But you won't use them as often. That's because you'll be able to control your computer with your voice! All you'll have to do is say "Homework," and the computer will display your homework on a screen.

And sometimes your computer will talk back! For example, it may "tell" you that the roof is leaking. Or that your 100-inch, 3-D television needs to be repaired. In the kitchen, all the appliances will be computer-controlled. When you open the refrigerator, it may tell you that you're running low on milk.

Your computer may even be hooked up to special devices that "watch" everything that goes on in your home. If you lie down for a nap, the computer will "see" it and dim the lights and close the blinds. Outside, a robot lawnmower will notice that the lawn has grown too long and will cut the grass while you relax. Built-in devices that can sense things will keep it from slamming into trees or running over the flowers.

Smart Clothes. Will future fashions look like the outfits worn in science-fiction movies? No one really knows. But whatever they look like, tomorrow's clothes will be "smart." They'll be made of special fabrics that will be able to sense the temperature and adjust to make you comfortable. They'll keep you cool in hot weather and warm in cold weather.

Clothes may even double as computers. Tiny computer chips will be put into the fabric. You'll be able to enter commands by tapping a pattern on your shirt! And your eyeglasses will be computer screens so you can see your wearable computer's output.

How will people be buying their computerized glasses and "smart" clothes hundreds of years from now? They'll probably do most of their shopping by computer. Millions of people already shop on the Internet. It's expected that millions more will be shopping that way in the future.

Cool Cars. Cars of the future will *really* be special. They won't cause air pollution as today's cars do. That's because they'll run on electricity, or on hydrogen fuel cells—which are used to power spacecraft today. And they'll be stuffed with high-tech features.

One device will check out traffic conditions and let you know if there are dangers ahead. Another device will measure the distance to the car ahead of you and warn you if you're getting too close. For night driving, special vision systems will help you detect things you might not see—like a dog running into the road. The system will detect the dog's warmth and warn you, giving you time to avoid it.

Your car may also have a system that makes sure you stay awake while you're driving. Mounted on the dashboard, this device will check your eyes for signs of sleepiness—and sound an ALARM if you start to nod off.

Fabulous Foods. How will the growing number of people in the world be fed? Experts are already predicting that there will be less farmland. So scientists will need to develop crops that don't need soil to grow. Instead, the crops will be grown in water containing lots of nutrients. High-rise, glass-enclosed water farms may be built right in the middle of busy cities.

Scientists are also trying to produce new kinds of foods. For example, they may be able to develop a potato with more vitamin C than an orange and more protein than a steak. Fry the potato in fat-free cooking oil, and you'll be eating french fries that are actually good for you!

There are lots of other predictions for the next millennium. People may learn to communicate with animals. They may set up colonies on the moon or make contact with alien beings. And they will surely invent things that we can't even imagine today!

MAKE WAY

Attention please! This blue-footed booby wants you to take a closer look at him and his comical cousins. Boobies may look clownish. But they are daredevil divers, devoted parents, and dazzling dancers.

A baby booby takes its first peek at the world.

The blue-footed booby would like some respect! This bird is pretty neat. It's an expert flier and a daredevil diver. And both the male and female are good parents. Yet people can't help laughing at it.

FOR THE BOOBY

Red-footed boobies are the only boobies that nest in trees.
The other boobies—like the blue-footed booby on the
opposite page—make their nests on the ground.

The sight of the bird waddling along on its big bright-blue webbed feet is just too funny.

It's also hard not to laugh at something called a "booby." How did the bird get that name? It probably comes from *bobo,* a Spanish word that means "stupid fellow." To early sailors, the booby was a *bobo* because it was so easy to catch. Boobies would land on ships and let sailors walk right up and grab them.

In addition to the blue-footed booby, there are five other kinds of boobies. They are alike in many ways. All boobies, for example, are big birds—about the size of a goose. They have long, graceful wings that stretch up to 5 feet from tip to tip. And the booby's streamlined body and long beak are perfectly designed for flying, diving, and eating.

On land, however, a booby's performance is another story. It touches down with the grace of a hippopotamus. Its big webbed feet, which are ideal for swimming in the ocean, aren't very good for walking. The bird clumsily waddles around, trying hard not to step on its own feet.

And then there's the boobies' amazing courtship dance (see the picture at left). The male blue-foot starts by pointing his bill and tail straight up and whistling. He rocks from side to side, picking up one blue foot and then the other. Soon the female joins in. The birds honk, dance, bow, nod, and touch bills. They even offer presents of twigs and pebbles to each other.

14

A pair of masked boobies preen (clean) each other while courting. These striking birds are very aggressive—they may even jab at each other in a mock fight during their courtship dance.

Female boobies lay from one to three eggs. Now those big booby feet come in handy. Unlike other birds, boobies don't sit on their eggs to keep them warm. They stand on them with their large feet! And for about a week after the eggs hatch, the chicks sit on their parents' feet. There, they are sheltered from cold winds and the hot sun.

Boobies nest along rocky shores in tropical and semitropical regions. Many live in the Galápagos Islands. These islands are in the Pacific Ocean, off the coast of South America. No people live there. But many researchers go there to study the birds. They have discovered that boobies are truly fascinating creatures that deserve to be admired.

Best Buddies

It was a hot day in the jungle, and Tarzan was spying on
Flynt and Mungo as they groomed each other for bugs.

"Flynt, you're covered in bugs!" grumbled Mungo.

"That's cuz I can handle 'em!" Flynt replied. "You just have
these little, bitty—Aaahk! What is that?"

Flynt pulled a matted ball of fur from Mungo's arm.

Just then Tarzan plopped down from a branch above. "Hi, guys!" he said. "You like my fake bug? I made it!"

"Hey, Tarzan," said Flynt, "go play with the babies!"

Tarzan turned away. Flynt and Mungo were his buddy Terk's friends. Tarzan just wanted them to like him, too. But he could tell that Flynt and Mungo thought he was weird. The only time they would let him hang around with them was when they needed him to do something they didn't feel like doing.

"Say, Flynt, let's go look
for some food," said Mungo.

"Can I go, too?" Tarzan asked.

"I guess so," said Flynt. "You can pick us some fruit."

"Yeah," said Mungo, "but first you gotta climb up that tree
over there and get the banana I put up there."

"Okay!" said Tarzan.

He scrambled up the tree as fast as he could. He thought he
was doing pretty well. He only slipped twice! But when he
reached the top, Tarzan couldn't find a banana anywhere.
Finally he called down.

"Hey, guys!" he cried. "I can't find the banana!"

It was Terk who finally answered Tarzan.

"Tarzan, that tree isn't a banana tree," she told him. "It doesn't grow bananas. You understand?"

"Yeah," said Tarzan, "but Mungo told me there was a banana up here, and—"

"Oh, Tarzan, that's Mungo's oldest trick!" Terk said. "He always says that when he's trying to get rid of somebody."

Tarzan sighed and slowly climbed back down the tree. When he got close to the bottom, he slipped and fell, landing right on top of Tantor.

"Yikes!" yelled Tantor. "Something's on my back!"

"Relax, Tantor," said Terk. "It's just Tarzan."

"Yeah," Tarzan giggled. "It's just me."

Tarzan began to feel better. He liked hanging out with Tantor and Terk. They were his two best buddies in the whole jungle.

"Say, guys, let's try to find Flynt and Mungo," Tarzan said.

"Now, why would you wanna do that?" asked Terk.

"Well, *you* have so much fun with them. If we find them, and we all play together, then maybe they'll find out that I'm fun, too. Then maybe they'll let me play with them."

Terk sighed. "All right," she said. "C'mon, Tantor, the three of us are goin' on an adventure."

"I'm not so sure about this," said Tantor. "Adventures have been known to cause contusions or concussions—or even possibly something cardiac in this heat."

"Tantor. . ." Terk said.

"Come on! Let's go," said Tarzan. "Flynt and Mungo said they were looking for fruit. Since it's so hot, I bet they were looking for something juicy, like coconuts."

The three friends headed toward a coconut grove. When they got there, they didn't find Flynt and Mungo. But they did find some half-eaten coconuts.

"I'll betcha Flynt and Mungo ate those!" cried Tarzan.

"Tarzan," Terk grumbled, "seein' half-eaten coconuts does not mean Flynt and Mungo have been here."

"But look!" said Tarzan, pointing at one of the coconuts. "Flynt always makes a hole in the top of the coconut to drink the milk out first. This one has a hole at the top."

Just then Tantor cried out. He had found some trampled brush at the edge of the clearing.

"Something big ran through here," he said in a shivery voice. "We'd better get out of here!"

"I'll bet that's where Flynt and Mungo went," Tarzan pointed out. "C'mon! I've gotta find them!"

Tarzan raced ahead, with Terk and Tantor following clumsily. Soon they came to a swamp. There were no trees. There were also no more broken branches.

"Oh, man," said Terk. "Now we've lost 'em for sure."

"This place is creepy," said Tantor. "Let's go home."

"Wait," said Tarzan. "Let's ask those storks if they've seen Flynt and Mungo."

"Tarzan, apes don't speak stork," said Terk.

"I do," said Tarzan. "I can speak stork."

Tarzan carefully approached one of the storks and began to speak. The stork told him that Flynt and Mungo had passed through the swamp a little while ago.

Tarzan thanked the stork, then moved on with Terk and Tantor. After a while they came to a muddy area, where they found footprints left by Flynt and Mungo. The footprints led straight to a big, hollow tree.

"Shhh," said Terk. "I'll bet they're hidin' in that tree."

It was too dark inside the tree to see anything. "Okay, Tantor," whispered Terk, "stick your trunk inside this tree and make the loudest noise you can."

"I can't," said Tantor. "How do I know what's inside—"

Before Tantor could finish, Terk grabbed his trunk and shoved it inside the tree. Terrified, Tantor trumpeted.

"Tantor!" cried Tarzan. "You did it!"

Six little baboons scrambled out of the hollow tree. Tarzan raced up to them and explained what had happened. Then

he asked them if they
had seen Flynt and Mungo.

The baboons chattered excitedly and
pointed toward a clearing. "Thanks, guys," Tarzan said.

When the friends arrived at the clearing, they found several
waterfalls. But there was no sign of Flynt or Mungo.

"C'mon, Tarzan, I'm gettin' tired of this," said Terk. "You
don't need to find those two apes, anyway. They're just gonna
make fun of you again. Who needs that?"

"Yeah, let's go home," Tantor suggested hopefully.

Tarzan looked at his friends. "You're right," he said. "I
couldn't ask for two better friends than you. Let's go cool off

by Elephant Falls, and then we'll head back. Forget about Flynt and Mungo."

Tarzan had his eye on a small pool of water just above one of the smaller waterfalls. A skinny tree on the shore looked as if it would lead to the pool. Tarzan quickly scrambled up the tree. But as he climbed, the little tree bent and cracked. Suddenly Tarzan was thrown through the sheet of water that cascaded down the cliff.

"Yeow!" cried Tarzan. He landed with a squishy splash on the other side of the waterfall—right in Flynt's lap!

"Tarzan!" cried Flynt. "How'd ya find us?"

"Ha, ha!" Mungo sniggered, pointing to the squished berries that Flynt had been eating. "You're a mess!"

"That's not funny," said Flynt. So he smeared juice all over Mungo, too. Now both apes were a mess.

"Hey, Tarzan," said Mungo. "Go get us some leaves so we can clean ourselves up."

Tarzan looked at Flynt and Mungo. Why had he spent so much time trying to find these guys? Suddenly he realized where he would rather be.

"Sorry," Tarzan replied. "My best friends are waiting for me." Then he leaped back through the waterfall.

As he walked toward Terk and Tantor, Tarzan thought about the way they had always accepted him just the way he was. Boy, was he lucky to have two best buddies like them!

SEALED IN STYLE!

If you make a special card, you'll need a special envelope
to put it in. Try making one of these envelopes. It's fun!

1. Lay your card in the middle of a big piece of paper. Fold the two sides of the paper in over the card.

2. Fold the bottom edge up over the card. Fold the top edge down. The card should fit perfectly inside.

3. Open the folds of the paper envelope. Cut out the corner rectangles, as shown here.

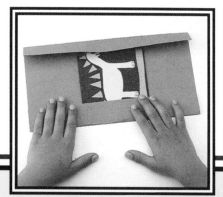

◀ This looks like an envelope. But it's really a letter folded in thirds and held together with a sticker.

Make a fancy envelope for a square card. Cut four flaps like flower petals. Fold them over the card, one flap at a time. Hold the flaps together with a colorful sticker.

4. Carefully fold slanted flaps on the top and bottom parts of the envelope.

5. Fold the sides of the envelope in. Fold the bottom up, and glue the flaps to the sides of the envelope.

6. Slip the card inside, and fold the top of the envelope down over it. Fasten with a favorite sticker.

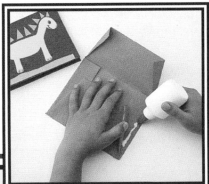

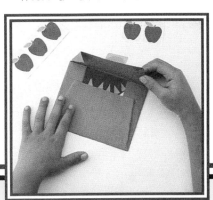

Around the World in 20 Days

A famous story tells how, in 1873, a gentleman named Phileas Fogg bet that he could go around the world in 80 days. Using ships, trains, sleds, carriages, elephants—and a hot-air balloon—Fogg did it, and won his bet. But Fogg wasn't a real person. He was the hero of *Around the World in Eighty Days*, a famous book that later became a movie.

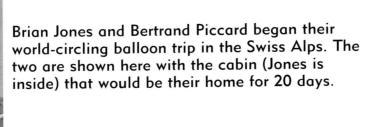

Brian Jones and Bertrand Piccard began their world-circling balloon trip in the Swiss Alps. The two are shown here with the cabin (Jones is inside) that would be their home for 20 days.

In 1999, Brian Jones of Britain and Bertrand Piccard of Switzerland became the first real-life heroes to circle the globe nonstop in a balloon. They did it in 20 days. Their daring balloon flight around the world was one of the greatest events in aviation history.

Jones and Piccard began their flight aboard the *Breitling Orbiter 3* balloon on March 1, in the Swiss Alps. They then flew south to North Africa to catch the jet streams. The jet streams are air

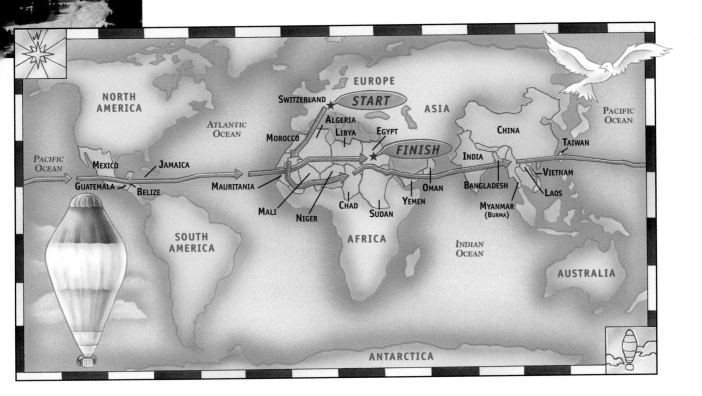

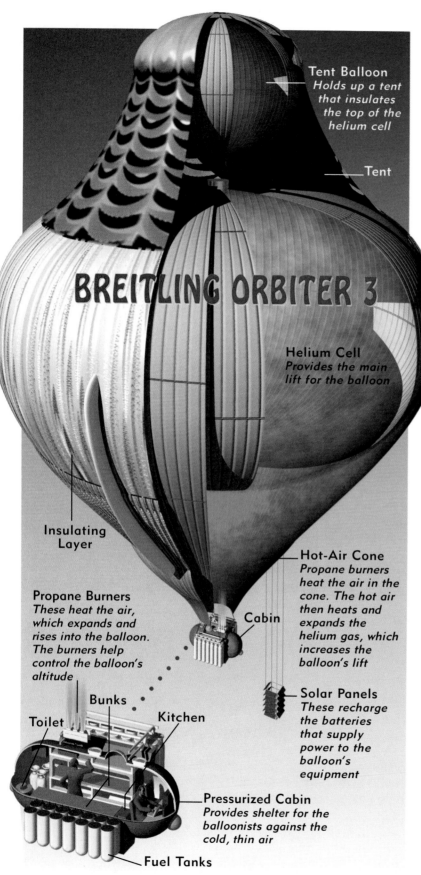

Tent Balloon
Holds up a tent that insulates the top of the helium cell

Tent

BREITLING ORBITER 3

Helium Cell
Provides the main lift for the balloon

Insulating Layer

Propane Burners
These heat the air, which expands and rises into the balloon. The burners help control the balloon's altitude

Hot-Air Cone
Propane burners heat the air in the cone. The hot air then heats and expands the helium gas, which increases the balloon's lift

Cabin

Bunks

Kitchen

Toilet

Solar Panels
These recharge the batteries that supply power to the balloon's equipment

Pressurized Cabin
Provides shelter for the balloonists against the cold, thin air

Fuel Tanks

currents that flow high above Earth, at speeds of up to 200 miles an hour. Piccard and Jones planned to ride these "rivers of air" across Africa, Asia, the Pacific Ocean, Central America, and the Atlantic Ocean.

The two men faced many dangers. They had to find their way around storms and mountains. And they worried that the jet stream would change course or even stop. But they had help. Ground crews used the latest weather

Ballooning Just for Fun

The *Breitling Orbiter 3* is a high-tech balloon that was designed to fly around the world. But some balloons, like the Mickey Mouse and Disneyland ones shown here, are made just for fun.

forecasting methods to help the balloon catch the most favorable winds. And satellites helped pinpoint the balloon's exact location at all times.

For much of the trip, Jones and Piccard traveled at an altitude of more than 6 miles. They rode in a special cabin, but it was so cold their water froze at night. Finally, on March 20, the balloon crossed the invisible finish line over Mauritania in northern Africa. The balloon continued on to Egypt, where it landed in the desert the next day. In all, the flight covered 29,055 miles in 19 days, 21 hours, and 55 minutes.

Piccard and Jones were exhausted but thrilled. "I am with the angels and just completely happy!" said Piccard. No wonder. He and Jones had just won the race to make the first nonstop balloon flight around the world!

This white **snake** is easy to spot on the forest floor. That's because it doesn't have the black and brown pigments that help normally colored snakes blend in. But look closely. You can see the traces of a ghostly pattern in its scales.

Peacocks are famous for their colorful, shimmering feathers. However, this albino peacock's feathers are pure white. In the wild, white feathers would make the bird easy for predators to spot. But this peacock lives among people, who protect it from danger.

COLOR ME WHITE

A cream-colored alligator? A pink and white koala? You'd expect to see such animals on a shelf in a toy store, not in nature. But these animals are real. They are albinos—animals that are white when they shouldn't be. Why are they white? Because

An albino **koala** snoozes in a eucalyptus tree. Its fluffy white fur and pink nose make it look like a little stuffed toy. But the koala must be very careful. Without pigment, that pink nose could get a very bad sunburn. It had better stay in the shade!

This albino **alligator** could also be harmed, even killed, by too much sun. That's a real problem for albino alligators because they are cold-blooded and need the sun's warmth to survive.

they don't have pigments. Pigments are the substances in skin, fur, feathers, and eyes that produce color.

There are all kinds of albino animals—including frogs, gorillas, penguins, and porcupines. And people have long been fascinated by them. American Indians even believed that albino deer and buffalo were sacred. It's easy to see why. There is something magical about these rare and wonderful creatures.

The Gray and Gloomy Day

Winnie the Pooh awoke feeling a little. . .a little. . .well, a little as if he didn't know how he felt. He sat up in bed and looked out the window. It wasn't raining, but it was a gray and gloomy day.

"This isn't at all the kind of day I had hoped it would be," he said to himself.

Pooh sighed. It was bad enough feeling the way he felt. But it was even worse not knowing exactly what it was that he was feeling. Pooh sat very still, trying to decide what the strange feeling was. But no matter how hard he thought, he just couldn't figure it out.

36

Finally, Pooh pulled himself from his snuggly bed.

"If anyone would know how a bear is feeling on such a gray day, Piglet would," he said to himself. So, tucking a jar of honey under his arm for the trip, Pooh went off to Piglet's house.

Piglet was home when Pooh arrived. He was in the kitchen opening drawers and peeking under things.

"Good morning, Piglet," called Pooh, hoping Piglet would invite him in.

"Good morning, Pooh," Piglet answered. But he continued his search. He was so busy, he didn't seem to realize that Pooh was there.

"Are you looking for something?" Pooh asked finally, having watched Piglet for some time.

"Yes," Piglet answered. "I keep a list of ways to cheer myself up on a gloomy day. And today being that kind of day, I thought I'd check my list."

"Oh," Pooh said. "And what does your list say?"

"I don't know!" Piglet squealed. "I can't find it!"

It was plain to see that Piglet had a problem of his own this morning. Pooh could also see that Piglet's problem was making him just a little grumbly.

Problems didn't make Piglet grumbly except on gloomy days.

So Pooh walked on, feeling a little. . .well, the same as he'd been feeling before.

Pooh hadn't gone far when he came upon Tigger. Tigger was sitting in the middle of the path, stretching and scrunching his tail. First he'd stretch it as far as it would stretch. Then he'd scrunch it as tightly as he could.

"Hello, Tigger," Pooh said.

Tigger looked up. "Oh, hello, Pooh. I'm having a little bounce trouble today."

"That's too bad," Pooh
answered. "Say, Tigger—"

"A tigger's bounce is a wonderful
thing, you know," Tigger went on.

"It is," Pooh agreed. "Tigger, would you know—"

"Without his bounce, a tigger is nothing," Tigger whispered to
Pooh.

Pooh sighed. The cloudy day had even taken the spring
out of Tigger's tail. It was clear that Tigger wouldn't
be any help, either.

Rabbit's house was just down the road. Pooh could see Rabbit standing in his garden. As he came closer, Pooh could hear Rabbit grumbling about what a gray day it was.

"My vegetables really need some sun!" Rabbit was harumphing. He stomped back and forth in his garden as he grumbled. "We haven't had a decent sunny day in weeks!"

Rabbit, who often sounded cross, sounded a little more cross than usual.

Pooh decided it wasn't the right day to ask Rabbit if he knew how a bear might be feeling.

At the end of the path, Pooh came to Owl's house. Owl was home, too, but he was fast asleep. It wasn't like Owl to sleep all day, but he was tucked down tight and looked as if he meant to stay that way.

Pooh found a comfortable spot to rest while he waited for Owl to wake up. After a while, waiting made him hungry, so he pulled out his honey jar to give himself a treat. On such a gloomy day, Pooh thought, a treat might be a good idea.

The honey *was* a good idea, but it didn't make the feeling go away, and Owl wasn't waking up.

"This gray day has gotten to everyone," Pooh said to himself. "Everyone is just too busy or too out of sorts to help me figure out how a bear might feel on such a day."

Now, feeling disappointed on top of everything else, Pooh decided to head home. So he turned and made his way back along the route he'd come—past Rabbit's house, past the spot in the road where Tigger was still working on his tail, past Piglet's house, and finally back to his own little home.

"On such a gray day, it might have been better if I had just stayed in bed," Pooh said to himself. He thought a moment. "Or maybe I'll go back to bed!" And with his honey jar in his arms, he did just that.

But no sooner had he climbed back into bed and snuggled down beneath his covers than Piglet, Rabbit, Tigger, and Owl appeared at the door!

"Well, hello, everyone!" Pooh called. His friends trooped in and stood around the bed.

MR

RNIG ALSO

"We just came by to see how you are, Pooh," Tigger said, and everyone nodded.

"You did?" said Pooh.

"Yes," returned Rabbit. "I'm afraid that I was making such a fuss about my garden earlier that I didn't even think to ask what you needed."

"And I was so busy looking for my list that I didn't even realize you were there," added Piglet.

"So what DID you need, Pooh?" Owl asked.

"Well," Pooh began, fumbling with the covers, "it was a cloudy day when I woke, and I was feeling a little. . ."

"Grumpy?" Rabbit suggested.

"Crabby?" asked Piglet.

"Growly?" Tigger said.

"No. . .not grumpy, not crabby, and not growly," Pooh answered thoughtfully. "I was feeling a little. . ."

"Sad," a voice cut in. Everyone turned to see who had said that. It was Eeyore, standing in the doorway. He'd come by looking for everyone else.

"On such a gloomy day, I often feel a little sad," Eeyore admitted, "as if I could use a hug."

"That's it EXACTLY!" Pooh shouted, jumping out of bed.

"Well, why didn't you say so?" Tigger laughed. With new spring to him, he bounced Pooh, Eeyore, Piglet, Rabbit, and Owl into one huge heap of hugs.

The friends stayed that way until all the sadness had been squished out of everyone. At last they pulled apart and sat down for a bit of tea and honey with Pooh.

"On such a gray and gloomy day, everyone needs a hug," Pooh said with a smile.

"A bear hug," Piglet offered.

"Yes, Piglet, a bear hug," Pooh sighed—happy now. It was great to have such good friends. Maybe the day hadn't ended up so gray and gloomy, after all.

Friends Forever

Hi, boys and girls! It's me—Mickey Mouse!

It's really great to have friends. They are the people who help us when we need it. Friends can be real people—our parents, our relatives, our neighbors, our classmates. Or they can be fantasy people—those we know from books and movies.

All my life, I've watched and read about the characters created by my friend Walt Disney and the animators in his studio. They've taught me and my friends Minnie, Goofy, Donald, and Daisy so much about life and how important friends are.

Walt created lots of wonderful stars for his feature films. Remember Snow White and the Seven Dwarfs? When Snow White was running from the wicked queen, the dwarfs opened their hearts and their home to her until her true love could find her. Boy, were they good pals!

Then there was Pinocchio. What a mischief-maker! It's a good thing he had his friend Jiminy Cricket to keep him on the straight and narrow, so the Blue Fairy could finally turn him into a real boy.

The next two I remember are Dumbo and Bambi, a young elephant and a young deer. Dumbo saved the circus, and Bambi saved the forest animals. Both of them knew plenty about friendship.

I always thought that if anybody deserved to live happily ever after, it was Cinderella. Of course, she had some help from Gus and Jaq. They were the ones who let Cinderella out of the attic when her stepmother was trying to keep her from trying on her glass slipper. We can all use friends like them.

"RRRRufff!"

What's that, Pluto? You want me to mention a couple of *your* favorites? Okay. How about Lady and

Tramp, Jock, and Trusty? No, Pluto, I'm not going to mention those Siamese cats. They weren't friendly at all. But I will mention Pongo and Perdita. Their friends were all the dogs of London, who helped them rescue 99 Dalmatian puppies from that awful Cruella De Vil!

Then there were Mowgli and Baloo, a boy and a bear, but still the best of pals. And what about Winnie the Pooh and all the others who live in the Hundred-

Acre Wood? They show us over and over what it means to be good friends.

More recently, I watched Ariel, a little mermaid, befriend a human prince by saving him from drowning. She fell in love with him, and they lived happily ever after. There's also a streetwise fellow named Aladdin who found out that

the best thing he could be was himself. He couldn't have done it without his big blue friend, the Genie. And then there's a beauty named Belle who taught a beast how to love.

Is there anyone who doesn't know the story of Simba, the Lion King? His friends Timon the meerkat and Pumbaa the

warthog not only saved his life, but also taught him how to enjoy it.

Watching these wonderful characters has taught me a lot about friendship. They've showed me that being a friend is the best way to make a friend. It's a wonderful lesson, and the best one we can take into the new millennium.

Go Fly A Kite

Can an elephant fly? The answer is "yes"—if it's a kite!
Kites also take the shapes of birds, stars, dragons, diamonds,
butterflies, and flowers. In fact, kites come in all shapes,
colors, and sizes. One kite, called Megabite, was almost as
long as a Boeing 747 airplane. Other kites are so small they
can fit in the palm of your hand.

But most people fly simple kites, such as the flat kite, the
bowed kite, and the box kite. These kites have been been
around for a long, long time—about 2,000 years!

54

The Chinese were probably the first people to fly kites. Even today, Kites' Day (or the Festival of Ascending High) is celebrated every year in that Asian country.

Kite flying is now popular around the world. Most of us do it for fun. But some people like to take part in kite-flying contests. And some of the records set by kite flyers are amazing.

One kite climbed to a height of more than 2 miles. It had a really long string! Another kite soared through the air at 120 miles per hour. How did the kite flyer keep up with it? And yet another kite stayed in the air for 180 hours, 17 minutes. That's 7½ days!

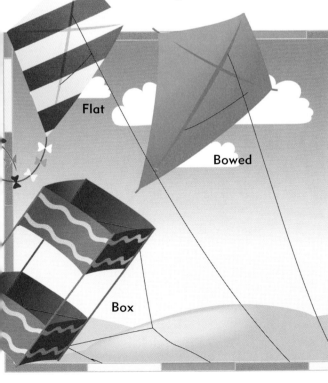

Flat

Bowed

Box

Kinds of Kites

The FLAT KITE is the oldest kind of kite. The weight of the tail helps keep the bottom of the kite down and the nose tilted up. The tail also keeps the kite steady in the air.

The BOWED KITE is one of the best fliers. It is built on a framework of two sticks crossed in a T. The cross stick is bent like an archer's bow.

The BOX KITE is shaped like a long box with open ends. The sides are covered except for an open section in the center.

How to Fly a Kite

The best time to fly your kite is on a clear day with gentle winds.

Ask a friend or a family member to help you launch your kite. Stand with your back to the wind, holding the flying line that's attached to the kite. Your friend should stand about 100 feet away, holding the kite upright at the corner. The front of the kite should be facing the wind.

Your friend should wait for a steady wind before letting go of the kite.

When the kite is let go of, pull in the line hand-over-hand. The kite will rise in the air.

To get your kite to fly higher and farther, pull in on the line and then let it out. Keep doing this.

To bring your kite down, walk toward the kite, in the direction in which the wind is blowing. Reel in the line as you walk.

Are you ready to get out there and watch your own kite sail in the breeze? Before you do, here are some very important safety rules for you to follow.

↪ Don't use any metal or wire in the kite or in the kite line. You could get a bad shock.

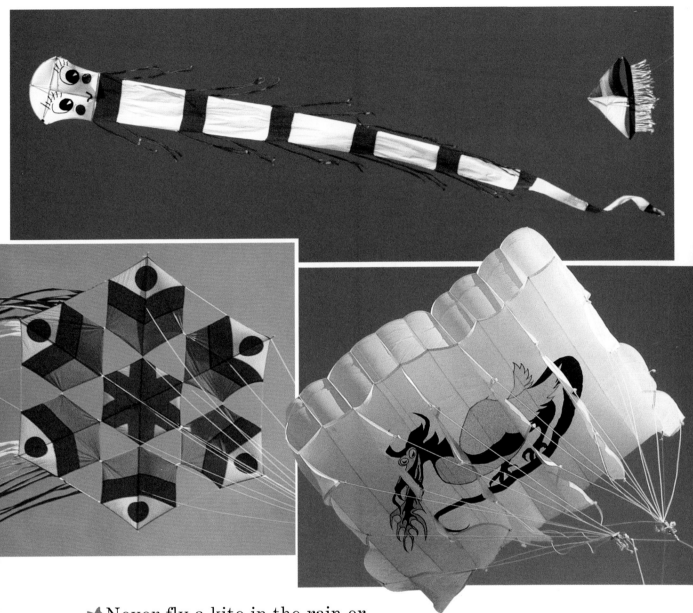

🐦Never fly a kite in the rain or during stormy weather.

🐦Don't fly a kite near antennas or electric wires or poles.

🐦Never try to rescue a kite if it's caught on a wire or pole.

🐦Don't fly a kite near the edge of a steep slope.

🐦On a very windy day, the kite line might pull through your hands quickly. So you might want to wear gloves.

OK, now you can go fly a kite!

A Place for Ariel

Ariel and her six sisters shared a bedroom in the palace. It was a large, beautiful room. But it was also a very crowded room. Ariel often felt as if she had no place for her own things and no privacy at all.

One day, as Ariel sat on her bed looking at the human objects she kept in her seashell box, her sisters came in.

"Ariel, you missed your voice lesson again. Sebastian is very crabby with you," Attina scolded.

"And look! You've scattered your hair combs and seashells all over the room again," Alana added.

"Why don't you keep your things tidy? We all have to share this room, you know," Arista complained as she stroked her pet sea horse.

"You're just as messy as I am," Ariel pointed out.

Her sisters shook their heads. "Oh, Ariel! You're such a merbaby," Attina said.

Ariel was tired of being lectured. "I'm going to find Flounder," she snapped. "At least he's not always fussing at me." She left in a huff, not realizing that her seashell box was still lying open on her bed.

"My sisters are driving me out of my fins," Ariel complained as she and Flounder swam along, looking for human treasures. "All I hear is 'Ariel, pick up your seashells. Ariel, put away your hair combs.' It's not fair. I wish I had a place all my own."

"I know what you mean, Ariel," Flounder replied. "Growing up in a school of fish doesn't exactly give me much privacy, either, you know."

Just then Ariel spied a shining circle of metal resting on the ocean floor. "Why, Flounder, this human object reminds me of my father's crown," she said, placing it on her head.

Delighted with her new treasure, Ariel hurried back to the palace. But when she entered her bedroom, she was very surprised to see her sisters and King Triton waiting for her. King Triton was holding her seashell box. And it was open.

"Ariel, where did you get these human objects?" Triton demanded angrily.

"Those are my treasures!" Ariel cried. "They were in my personal, private box. No one had any right to look in it!"

"You left it out for anyone to see," Arista told her. "We couldn't help seeing what was in it."

"And when they saw what you were hiding, your sisters

61

came to me at once," Triton added. "They were worried about you. And so am I. You know I don't want any human objects in my palace."

Ariel's sisters agreed.

"You're all a bunch of snoops and tattletales!" Ariel cried, as she grabbed her seashell box. "Come on, Flounder, we're leaving!" Blinking back tears of anger, Ariel swam from the

room. Flounder followed silently. For a long time they swam, traveling farther and farther from the palace. Flounder began to get nervous.

"Ariel, we're awfully far from home," he said timidly. "Don't you think we should turn back?"

Ariel was about to call
Flounder a guppy when she spied
something. "A coral forest!" she cried.
"There'll be lots of wonderful hiding places for us! And there
won't be any snoopy, sneaky big sisters anywhere around!"

"There might be snappy, snarly big sharks around,
though!" Flounder pointed out.

But Ariel wasn't listening. She was twisting in and out of
the forest of pink and purple coral, exploring nooks and
crannies, finding little tunnels and hideaways. Flounder
followed her timidly. Neither of them noticed the pair of cold
yellow eyes that watched them from the shadows. Neither of
them heard the swoosh of a giant tail gliding closer and
closer behind them.

Suddenly—SNAP! Huge jaws snapped at Flounder's tail.
"Ariel! Shark! Shark!" Flounder shrieked.

Ariel and Flounder swam for their lives, twisting and turning
through the coral branches. But the shark was always just a
few feet behind them. Suddenly Ariel saw a high wall of coral
just ahead. And in the wall was a narrow crack—just big
enough for them to squeeze through. Ariel pushed Flounder
through the crack and squeezed in behind him. On one side of
the wall was the snapping shark. Just ahead of them was a
long, dark tunnel.

"I d-d-don't like it here," Flounder said. "Long, dark tunnels
make me dizzy."

"Well, tunnels are a whole lot better than sharks," Ariel replied.

Just then the shark bashed its tail against the wall. The crack widened, and chunks of coral crashed down. The crack widened some more.

"Ariel, do something!" Flounder pleaded as the shark pushed its snout through the wide crack in the wall. It snapped its terrible teeth at them.

Quickly Ariel grabbed the shiny metal circle from her head and jammed it over the shark's jaws, clamping them shut.

The shark snarled and thrashed as it tried to pry the circle from its jaws. Its tail hit the wall again. This time the coral crumbled completely. Falling chunks knocked Ariel and Flounder away.

With a fearful cry, they darted into the tunnel. Twisting and turning, they reached the end. They were in a tiny grotto! The floor was soft and sandy. Above them, light streamed down

through the broken
wall. Little nooks and
crannies and tiny shelves
had formed here and there
in the walls of soft, pastel-
colored coral that
surrounded them.

Unable to enter the grotto,
the shark snarled and swam
away.

"Say good-bye to old greedy
jaws!" Flounder said with a
sigh of relief.

"I think that shark did me a
favor, Flounder," Ariel replied.

"He did?" Flounder was
surprised.

"Yes. We never would have found this grotto if he hadn't chased us," Ariel explained. "And just look! It's a perfect place of my own. Why, I can keep my human treasures here and not worry about making Daddy angry." Humming happily, Ariel arranged her human objects around the grotto. Then she and Flounder headed back to the palace.

Ariel was so happy she didn't even mind when she saw her father and sisters waiting for her. Ariel's sisters rushed to greet her. "We were worried about you," Attina said. "We're all sorry we snooped, but guess what! Daddy's decided we need more space, so he's going to build each of us a new bedroom!"

"That's right, Ariel." King Triton smiled at his youngest daughter. "After all, every daughter needs a special place of her own!"

"Or even two special places," Ariel whispered to Flounder with a wink. Then, with her head full of happy plans for her two special places, Ariel gave her father the biggest hug he had had all day.

POLKA-DOT PICTURES

A springtime cherry tree. A sprig of berries. A bubbling fish. An ice-cream cone. A bunch of flowers. All these pictures are made with lots and lots of paper dots.

You will need a hole-punch and different-colored papers to make the dots.

Now draw a design on a sheet of paper. Use white glue or a glue stick to carefully paste the dots onto your design. If you slightly overlap the dots, you will get a 3-D effect.

Use colored markers to create details such as flower stems, a tree trunk, an ice-cream cone, and the smile of a fish.

THE NOSE KNOWS!

This monkey's nose is so long that it hangs down over its mouth. That's why it's called a proboscis monkey. "Proboscis" means "long snout"! The proboscis monkey uses its huge, drooping nose to increase the loudness of its calls.

Animal noses aren't just for sniffing. They perform a huge number of jobs. They are used to dig, cut, drill, crack, and spray. Some animals rely on their noses to greet friends, warn off enemies, fight, spank youngsters, or capture prey.

The male proboscis monkey, for example, uses his huge nose to scare away enemies. His nose makes the sounds of his calls louder and scarier. It acts sort of like an echo chamber.

An even bigger nose is an elephant's trunk—it can be up to 6 feet long! And no nose is more useful. The elephant can use its trunk to lift a ton of logs or to pick up a tiny peanut. And since its nose is shaped like a rubber hose, it can bend in almost any direction to test for interesting smells.

On hot days, an elephant uses its trunk to spray cool water across its ears and back. It also sucks up sand with its trunk and blows it over its body to help keep biting insects away.

When friendly elephants meet, they twist their trunks together in an affectionate elephant greeting. That's just one use of their talented trunks.

And an elephant "talks" through its trunk, using it to scream with rage or squeal with pleasure. Mother elephants cuddle their babies with a soft touch of their trunks. They punish them with a swift, hard whack.

The little elephant shrew's snout is a great insect-sniffer.

Another extra-long nose belongs to the little elephant shrew. It has a trunk like an elephant and long hind legs like a kangaroo. But it's no bigger than a rat. The elephant shrew uses its nose to sniff for insects on the forest floor.

A bird's nose is where its mouth is. Its beak or bill is actually a combination of nostrils and lips. The beak is important to a bird because it acts as both a tool and a hand. The brightly colored beak of the South American toucan is especially useful. It has sawtooth edges that can slice and dice fruits, insects, lizards, and small snakes. And the toucan uses its beak to reach for fruit that might otherwise be hard to get.

As you can see, the toucan's beak is also very long—

The toucan's curved beak is excellent for picking and slicing fruit.

sometimes as long as the rest of its body. But the inside of the bulky beak is filled with air pockets. So it's almost as light as foam rubber. If it were any heavier, the big-beaked toucan would fall on its nose!

The spoonbill's beak looks like a long serving spoon. And it uses its beak like a spoon—to get food. When feeding, the bird

A spoonbill's beak looks like a long serving spoon. It uses its beak to catch small fish, insects, and other food in shallow waters.

moves its beak from side to side, catching small fish and insects. The spoonbill also uses its beak to make clapping noises when it returns to the nest and greets its mate.

The Jackson's chameleon of Africa uses its nose as a weapon. It has a pointed horn at the tip of its snout, with two other

Even with a baby sitting atop its head, the Jackson's chameleon appears ready to defend its territory with its horned snout.

horns just above it. If a rival enters its territory, this chameleon charges at it nose first.

The spatulate-nosed tree frog uses its hard, bony nose to protect itself. Its nose is shaped like a flat spoon, or spatula. When the weather is hot and dry, the frog finds a hole among rocks or in a tree and crawls inside. Then it plugs up the

The spatulate-nosed tree frog uses its spoon-shaped nose to protect itself in hot, dry weather.

76

entrance with its flat nose. Protected from the sun, the frog is able to stay cool and moist.

The prize for the strangest-looking nose of all goes to the star-nosed mole. This animal, which lives underground and is nearly blind, has 22 fleshy feelers around its nostrils. They wiggle constantly as the mole searches for worms and insects to eat.

The star-nosed mole takes top prize for the weirdest-looking nose. This animal has 22 fleshy feelers forming a ring around its nostrils.

While its nose may look odd, it really works. A star-nosed mole finds and eats half its weight in insects every day.

Your nose might not be able to do as many things as some animal noses. But you couldn't breathe or smell without it!

To the Future and Back

Early one morning, many, many years from now. . .

"WAAAK!" Donald Duck squawked. His fully automatic, quicker-getter-upper bed flipped over and dumped him on the floor. "I'll never get used to that bed," he muttered, staggering toward the bathroom.

His new Bathroom of the 21st Century had been installed just yesterday. Daisy Duck insisted he have the latest, most modern space-age bathroom. The company that created the Bathroom of the 21st Century was the biggest account at Daisy's advertising agency. Her award-winning slogan— "Fresh as a Daisy"—had made Daisy a trillionaire.

Donald sighed, entered the bathroom, and pressed the start button. "Good morning, Mr. Duck," said a computer voice. The bathroom whirled into action. Robot arms removed Donald's pajamas and squeezed toothpaste onto his toothbrush. Another pair of arms brushed his teeth, then placed him in the wash-and-fluff-o-rama shower. "Ah," sighed Donald. Not-too-hot, not-too-cold water doused him from all sides. "This is wonderful!" The automated shower washed, shampooed, fluff-dried, and bathrobed him in two minutes flat.

One innovation that
Donald would not let
Daisy install was the Automatic
Dresser of the 21st Century. He had his
own special style of dressing.

Donald left the house and hailed a passing helicopter-taxi. He was meeting Daisy for breakfast at Clarabelle's Cafe.

"Good morning, Donald dear," Daisy called. "How's your Bathroom of the 21st Century?"

"Fresh as a Daisy!" said Donald. Daisy laughed and ordered her breakfast. Clarabelle gave the order to her electronic hands-free order pad. "That's one Daisy Duck special—wheat-grass-vitamin-super-synthetic-organic-power-shake."

Ten minutes later, Donald dropped Daisy off at her office, and then took the heli-cab to the *Miss Daisy 2001*.

"Good morning, Captain," said the computer voice when Donald stepped on board. As the *Miss Daisy* headed out to sea, the automatic fishing poles saluted their captain, then baited their own hooks, cast the line out, and reeled in the fish. Soon they started tossing fish into the tank. Donald paced the deck, looking for something to do.

Fishing used to be an adventure, thought Donald, as he sighed. "This is kind of. . .boring—WAAK!" he cried.

A bottle fished from the sea whacked him on the head.

"What a strange-looking bottle," Donald muttered. "I wonder
what's inside. Maybe it's a genie who will grant me three
wishes!"

Donald opened the bottle, and colored smoke drifted
skyward. Lights flashed. . .but no genie. Then the smoke
cleared and a computer screen appeared.

"This is the genie. I'm sorry I'm not in to grant your wishes.
Due to the high volume of bottle-wishing, only one wish can be
granted at this time. Please select from the following options:
Press Button 1 for romance, 2 for adventure, and 3 for. . ."

"Adventure! Oh, boy!" said Donald, quickly pressing Button
2. In the blink of an eye, Donald found himself in front of an
old-fashioned log cabin next to a lake.

Donald spotted a fishing pole and jumped into a canoe. "It's been a long time since I paddled a can. . .OOF! WAAK!" cried Donald, as he fell into the lake. "Brr!" He shivered, struggling back into the canoe.

Donald dropped the fishing line into the water. In just a few minutes he felt a tug. "A bite!" Soon Donald had landed the fish and paddled back to shore. "Ah, this is the life!" he said.

Inside the cabin, Donald saw a small pile of wood next to an old wood-burning stove. "Hmmm. I think I need some more wood," he said to himself.

Behind the cabin, Donald
loaded himself up with firewood. But as he
staggered toward the door, he tripped. The wood went
flying. "Yeow!" he cried.

Donald stumbled into the cabin and loaded all the wood into
the stove. Then he found some strips of cloth to wrap around
his bruised head. He took off his wet sailor suit and hung it
over the stove.

Donald was cleaning the fish when he smelled smoke. "Yikes!
My sailor suit!" he cried. He grabbed his suit just before it
caught fire.

While the fish cooked, Donald went out and found a field of
wild strawberries. "Yum!" he cried, filling his sailor cap with
the juicy, ripe berries.

Unfortunately, a family of bears was also picking berries.
One look from mama bear sent Donald racing back to the
cabin, right through a patch of thorn bushes. "Ouch! Ow!
Yeow!" he cried.

All in all, it hadn't been the best morning of Donald's life.
But none of his misadventures could keep Donald from cooking
up his favorite dish, fish à la strawberries. He was just about
to take a bite, when. . . .

Suddenly Donald found himself
back on the *Miss Daisy 2001!* His fish à la
strawberries had completely disappeared. He was left
holding the bottle. The tank was full of fish, and his boat
was heading slowly back to the dock.

"Where's my fish à la strawberries?" Donald complained.
"Where's my log cabin? What happened?"

Colored smoke from the bottle drifted skyward, lights
flashed. . .but again, no genie. The genie's voice mail said,
"We're sorry. Your wish has been deleted due to computer
malfunction. Unfortunately, terminated wishes cannot be
granted again. We are sorry for any inconvenience this may
have caused. Please return the bottle to the sea so that we
may serve others." Donald threw the bottle overboard and
stomped off the boat.

"Donald!" cried Daisy when she met him that evening at Clarabelle's Cafe. "What happened? Your head is bandaged! Your face and arms are scratched! Your suit is burned, and your cap is stained red!"

Donald explained all about the bottle, the wish, the canoe, the log cabin, the wood-burning stove, the wild strawberries, the thorn bushes, and the bears—and what a great time he had had!

"You mean it was fun to fall in a lake, drop wood on your head, burn your clothes, run through thorn bushes, get chased by bears, and cook your own food?" Daisy asked.

"Well," Donald said, "some parts were more fun than others."

"Would you pay money to do it all over again?" Daisy asked. Her eyes twinkled with the spark of an idea.

"Sure," Donald said. "But the chances of finding that genie's bottle again—"

"What should I call it?" Daisy wondered out loud.

"Call what?" asked Donald.

"The theme park," she replied.

"What theme park?" Donald asked.

"An adventure theme park," Daisy explained, "where visitors do all the things that 21st-century machines do now.

I'll have a lake for fishing, canoes, fields of wild berries, and log cabins with wood-burning stoves. I could even put in mechanical bears in the berry fields."

When Clarabelle came over to take their orders, Daisy got up. "Where are you going?" Donald asked.

"Back to the office," Daisy said. "This idea is fabulous. I'll get started right away!"

Donald sighed. Then he looked at Clarabelle. "I'll have the fish à la strawberries, please."

This is what the *International Space Station* will look like when it's completed in 2005. Outside, huge solar panels will provide the station with power. Inside the station, there will be as much room as in two jumbo jets.

The International Space Station

It will be as big as a football field, and it will float 200 miles above Earth! What is it? It's the *International Space Station (ISS)*—an orbiting lab where seven astronauts will be able to live and work for as long as six months at a time. And it will be one of the most exciting projects of the 21st century!

Sixteen countries have joined together to build and use this gigantic space station. The United States and Russia, the world's leaders in space exploration, are doing much of the work. But Canada, Japan, and members of the European Space Agency are helping.

The *ISS* will be made up of several units, or modules. It will take at least 43 space flights to get all the units assembled and connected to each other. The first two units were sent up in 1998. The third unit was sent up in 1999. The last unit to be sent up will be the living quarters for the astronauts and scientists.

Suppose you could visit the space station. What would it be like? For one thing, you wouldn't feel Earth's gravity, or pull. So anything that wasn't tied down—including you!—would just float around. The only way to stay in one spot would be to wear a seat belt or slip your feet into holders attached to the floor.

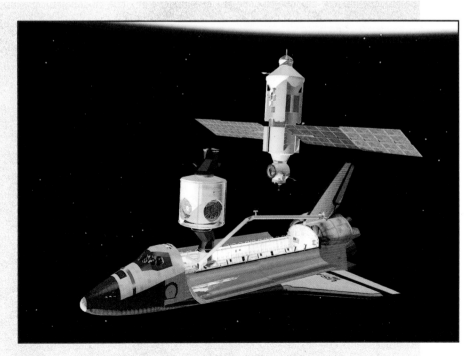

The Russian-built *Zarya* and the U.S.-built *Unity* were the first two units of the *ISS* to be sent aloft. This drawing shows how the space shuttle *Endeavour* carried *Unity* into space. The astronauts in the shuttle are preparing to use the shuttle's robot arm to capture *Zarya* and attach it to *Unity*.

Life aboard the space station will definitely be an adventure for astronauts! Doing everyday things like eating and bathing is a real challenge when there's no gravity—and no up or down. (Will that food-filled floating fork ever reach the astronaut's mouth?)

Without gravity, there's no difference between up and down. To help crews feel at home, the space station will have "make-believe" ups and downs. Lights will be on "ceilings," and tables will be attached to "floors."

Some hard jobs will be easy in this weightless world. You'll be able to lift heavy objects, even another crew member, with a fingertip. But easy jobs will be hard

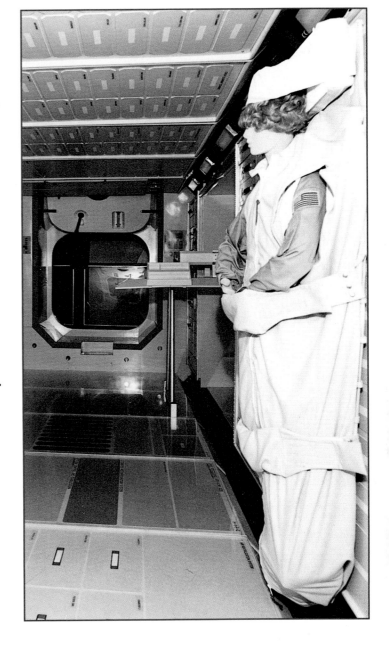

Sleeping won't be so easy, either. Would you be able to sleep in a pod that's hanging from a wall?

because nothing stays where you put it. If you want to make a peanut-butter sandwich, someone will have to hold the jar while you spread the peanut butter on the bread.

Meals will be different from those on Earth. Most food will be pre-cooked, packed in pouches, and freeze-dried (frozen and dried) so it will weigh less. Special equipment will add water and warm the food before it's eaten. Drinks can't be poured into cups, so you'll use straws to sip your drink from a pouch. If your drink spills, don't worry. The liquid will form a perfect sphere that floats in the air. You'll just suck it up with your straw.

There won't be any lounge chairs on the space station. When you want to relax, all you'll have to do is float for a while. There won't be beds, either. When there's no up or down, you don't need to lie down to sleep. But you will need to be tied down—or you'll float! So space-station astronauts will tuck themselves into sleeping pods that look something like hanging sleeping bags. There will also be a toilet and a shower. The toilet will use air suction to pull waste into a tank. And in the shower, airflow will keep water moving down and out the drain. Since water will be in short supply, it will be purified and used again.

Skylab and Mir

The *ISS* isn't the first space station. *Skylab* (shown at right) was launched by the United States in 1973. Three groups of astronauts spent some time aboard the space station. The longest stay was 84 days. *Skylab* later began to lose altitude. In 1979 it crashed in the Indian Ocean and Australia.

Mir, a Russian space station, has been orbiting Earth since 1986. The Russian cosmonauts aboard *Mir* were often joined by astronauts from other countries. In 1994–95, Russian cosmonaut Valery Polyakov stayed aboard *Mir* for more than 437 days— setting the all-time record for living in space. But *Mir* was getting old, and in 1999, Russia announced that it would abandon the 13-year-old station. *Mir* will soon leave outer space and burn up in the atmosphere, with parts of it crashing in the Pacific Ocean.

Working on the *ISS* will call for lots of space walks. For that, the astronauts will need special space suits.

What will the scientists and astronauts do on the *ISS?* They will learn how to live and work in space for long periods of time. They will study what weightlessness does to humans and animals. And they will research materials that behave differently when there's no gravity. This may help them find better ways of producing everything from medicines to computer chips.

It will take special kinds of people to live and work in space. But the hope is that the *International Space Station* will show how nations can work together for the benefit of all. And one day the *ISS* may serve as the jumping-off point for long space missions. . .to the moon, to Mars, or beyond!

THE JOKE'S ON YOU!

What goes oom, oom?
A cow walking backward!

How does a cat stop a VCR?
It pushes the "paws" button!

What do pigs put in their computers?
Sloppy disks!

What room has no doors, no floor, no windows, and no ceiling?
A mushroom!

What did the kangaroo say when her baby was missing?
Help! Someone picked my pocket!

Why did the Dalmatian go to the dry cleaner?
Its coat had spots on it!

What does a flower call its best friend?
Bud-dy!